3

"Gran," said Becky.

"You need a dog.

A dog will make you happy."

"Yes!" smiled Gran.

"A dog **will** make me very happy."

"Come on!" said Becky.
"Let's go to Mrs Pot's Animal Shelter.
They have lots of dogs."

So off they went!

5

Yip! Yip!

Woof!

It was **very** noisy
at Mrs Pot's Animal Shelter.

Mrs Pot took them to see
all the dogs.

"I like this dog," said Gran.
A little brown dog with a pink nose
looked at Gran.

"Oh!" said Mrs Pot.
"That dog is a good dog,
but it runs and runs.
That dog is too fast for you!"

"Oh, dear," said Gran.

"I like this dog," said Gran.
Then she patted a big black dog
with a long tail.

"Oh!" said Mrs Pot.
"That dog likes to dig and dig.
That dog will dig up your garden."

Gran looked sad.

"Mmmmm," she said.

"That's not good."

Gran looked at a little fluffy dog.

"I like this dog," said Gran.

"Oh!" said Mrs Pot.

"That dog likes to jump."

"Good!" said Gran.
"That little dog is for me.
I like **that** little dog."

And with that, Becky opened
the gate.
The little dog ran over to Gran
and **jumped** onto her lap.

"Yes!" laughed Becky and Belle.
"**That** little dog likes you, too!"